John Thompson's Easiest Piano Course

PART ONE

Exclusive distributors:
Music Sales Limited, 8-9 Frith Street, London W1V 5TZ.
Music Sales Pty Limited, 120 Rothschild Avenue, Rosebery, NSW 2018, Australia.

Order No. WMR000297

Printed and bound in the United Kingdom by Printwise (Haverhill) Limited, Haverhill, Suffolk.

The Willis Music Co.

CONTENTS

FOREWORD

PURPOSE

This Course is designed to present the easiest possible approach to Piano Playing.

Part One is devoted to developing fluency in *reading by note*, solving a problem that still seems to rate as "Musical Enemy, Number One" with most young students.

The Work Sheets together with the Reading Aloud Exercises, appearing frequently, afford plenty of drill even for the backward student.

SCOPE

The range covered in Part One is purposely limited. Only five notes up and five notes down from Middle C are presented and Time Values do not go beyond Crotchets. This makes it possible to include many examples in the form of Review Work and obviates the necessity of using supplementary material. In short, each book of the Course is complete in itself and contains its own Writing Exercises, Sight Reading Drills, Review Work and (in later books) Technical Studies.

ACCOMPANIMENTS

Accompaniments for teacher or parent are supplied with most of the examples. They have been carefully composed to make the little pieces sound as much as possible like fragments from larger compositions. Valuable in several ways, they not only make it possible to play in various keys, avoiding the deadly monotony of C major, but their use imposes strict Time and sharp Rhythm, especially when they are played with somewhat vigorous accents, thus helping the pupil to "feel" the rhythm from the very beginning.

GRADING

The Books in this Course do not represent any certain grade. They simply follow in proper sequence as Part One, Part Two, Part Three, etc. Nor are the Lessons measured page by page. Some pupils will master several pages per lesson—others only one. The Course progresses "Point by Point" rather than "Lesson by Lesson," and it is left to the teacher (who, after all, is the only one qualified) to decide how much or how little each pupil can absorb in one lesson.

PART TWO

Part Two proceeds from the exact point reached at the end of Part One. New Notes, Time-Values and Rudiments are presented. Technique also begins in Part Two—first in the form of simple Finger Drills and later, more extended technical figures. Part Two remains in what is generally classified as Preparatory Grade.

The prime objective of the entire Course is to show *how easily, thoroughly, entertainingly* and *musically*—rather than *how fast*—each pupil can progress.

John Thompson

THE PIANO KEYBOARD

There are WHITE KEYS and BLACK KEYS on the Piano Keyboard.

The WHITE KEYS are named

Recite the letters of the Musical Alphabet several times.

The BLACK KEYS are grouped in TWOS and THREES.

Touch all the groups of TWO BLACK KEYS on your piano.

THIS IS HOW TO FIND C ON YOUR PIANO

C is found to the *left* of the TWO BLACK KEYS.

Letter all the C's you can find on the Keyboard Chart, next page.

Now, on your piano, PLAY all the C's you can find—using the thumb.

W.M.Co. 7259

KEYBOARD CHART

(A section of the Keyboard)

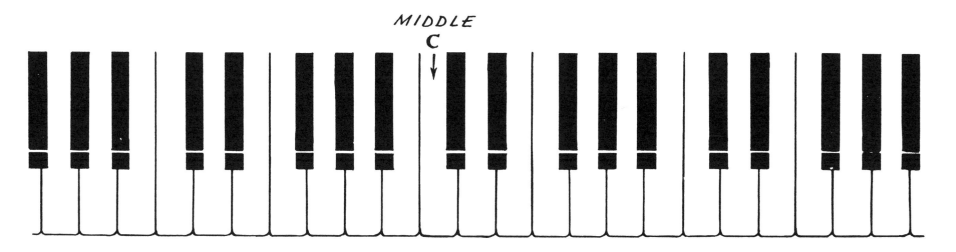

MIDDLE C ON THE MUSIC

The Staff

Music is written on the LINES and SPACES of the STAFF.

The NOTES on the Music tell us which KEYS to play.

There are different kinds of Notes, but first we shall learn the SEMIBREVE.

A SEMIBREVE looks like this, **O**

It is held for FOUR COUNTS.

Clef Signs

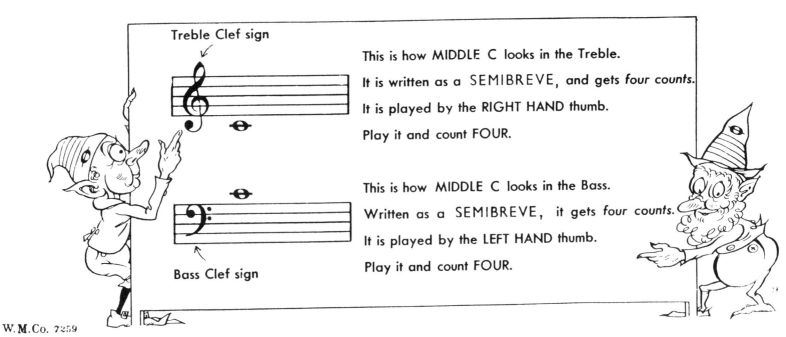

Treble Clef sign

This is how MIDDLE C looks in the Treble.

It is written as a SEMIBREVE, and gets *four counts*.

It is played by the RIGHT HAND thumb.

Play it and count FOUR.

This is how MIDDLE C looks in the Bass.

Written as a SEMIBREVE, it gets *four counts*.

It is played by the LEFT HAND thumb.

Play it and count FOUR.

Bass Clef sign

MUSIC IS DIVIDED BY BAR LINES INTO BARS.

Bar Line   Bar Line   Bar Line

Bar   Bar   Bar   Bar

The figures after the Clef Signs tell us how to count.

In this book we need only read the *top* figure.

It shows how many counts to each bar.

Count 4 to each bar

Count 3 to each bar

Count 2 to each bar

Left Hand

Each finger has a number.   The thumbs are number 1.

Right Hand

Middle C as a Semibreve
In the Treble

Accompaniment

PLAY WITH RIGHT HAND THUMB
COUNT FOUR TO EACH NOTE

Let's Play
With the Right Hand

Middle C as a Semibreve

In the Bass

Accompaniment

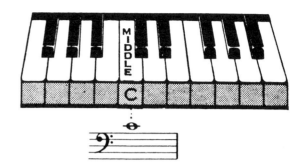

Let's Play

With the Left Hand

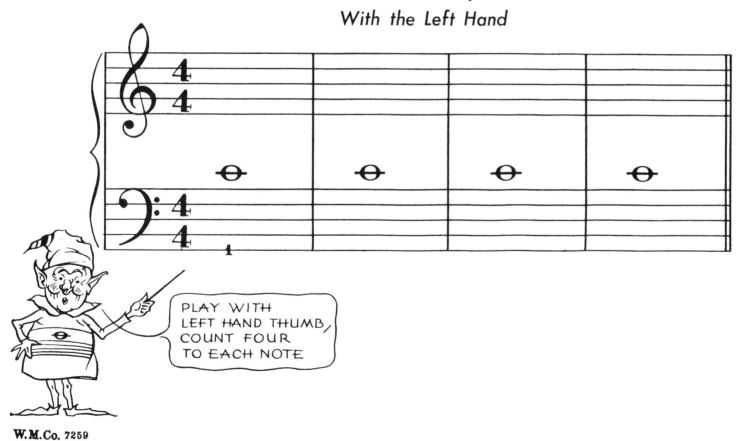

W.M.Co. 7259

Middle C in Minims

When a Note has an open head and a stem, like this, (𝅗𝅥 or 𝅗𝅥) it is called a MINIM and gets *two counts*.

Play the following, counting TWO to each note—"ONE, TWO" to the first note and "THREE, FOUR" to the second note of each bar.

Grandfather's Clock

Middle C in Crotchets

A CROTCHET looks like this (♩ or ♩) and gets *one count*.

Moccasin Dance

Count: One Two Three Four

Accompaniment

WORK SHEET

Mark the Time Values of the following notes, using 1 for Crotchets, 2 for Minims and 4 for Semibreves.

1

Make Minims of the following by adding stems.

Stems Up

2

Stems Down

Change the following into Crotchets by filling in the heads and adding stems when necessary.

3

Write Middle C in each Clef.

4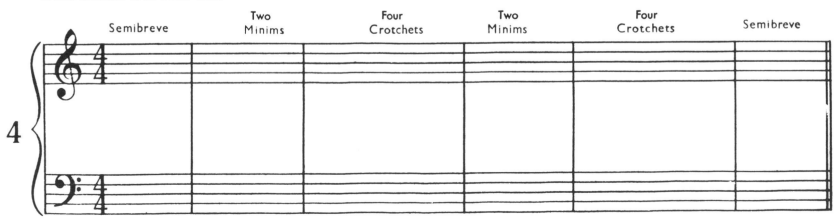

Accompaniment

R. H. New Note

The Train

TURN TO THE WORK SHEET ON PAGE 15 AND DO EXERCISES 1 AND 2

Note to Teacher

From this point on, be sure to stress the importance of accenting the first count of each bar.

W.M.Co. 7259

Accompaniment

The Seabées

DO WRITING EXERCISES 3, 4 AND 5 ON PAGE 15

SEABÉES: A descriptive word-play on the U.S. Navy's CONSTRUCTION BATTALION who are busy as bees when tackling a difficult task.

WORK SHEET

Write the letter names under the notes.

1

Write the new note (D) as indicated.

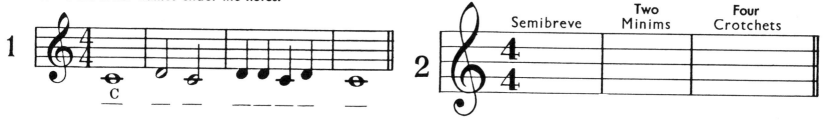

2

| Semibreve | Two Minims | Four Crotchets |

Write the letter names under the notes.

3

C

Write the new note (B) as indicated.

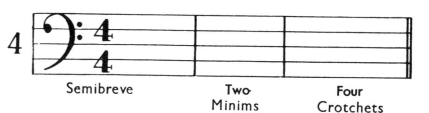

4

| Semibreve | Two Minims | Four Crotchets |

In the following exercise, first draw the Bar Lines where they belong.   (note Time Signature).

Next write the letter names of the notes.

Finally, mark the Time Values—using 1 for a Crotchet, 2 for a Minim and 4 for a Semibreve.

5

Letter Names C ___ ___ ___ ___ ___ ___ ___ ___

Time Values 2 ___ ___ ___ ___ ___ ___ ___ ___

W.M.Co. 7259

Accompaniment

TWO-FOUR

COUNT TWO TO EACH BAR.

March of the Gnomes

THREE-FOUR
and
The Dotted Minim

The dotted minim.

looks like this (or)

and is held for 3 counts.

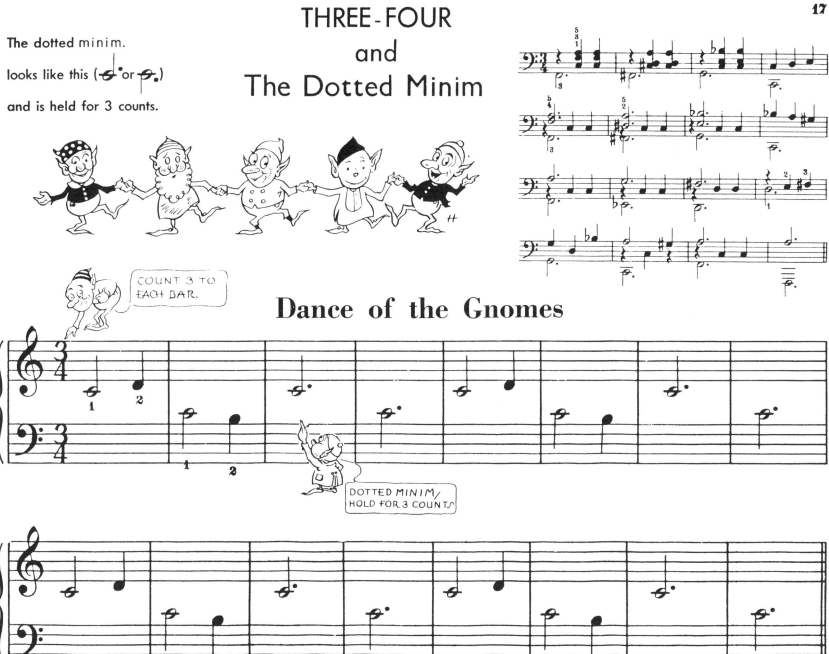

COUNT 3 TO EACH BAR.

Dance of the Gnomes

DOTTED MINIM/ HOLD FOR 3 COUNTS

See the importance of correct counting? These are the same notes you played in "March of the Gnomes" but they make a new piece when you count 3 to each bar.

W.M.Co. 7259

Read Aloud

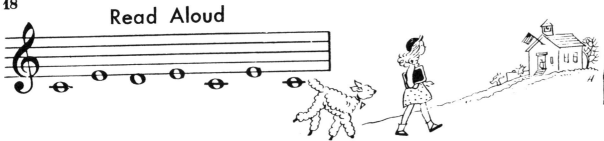

New Note

Mary Had a Little Lamb

Write the new note (E) below.

Accompaniment

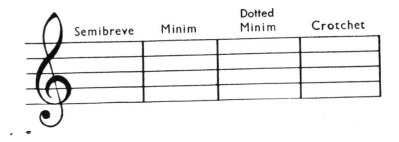

Semibreve	Minim	Dotted Minim	Crotchet

W.M.Co. 7259

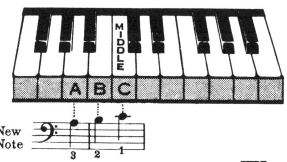

New Note

The Paratrooper

Read Aloud

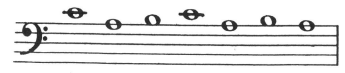

Write the new note (A) below.

Semibreve	Minim	Dotted Minim	Crotchet

W.M.Co. 7259

20

Read Aloud

Marching Up and Down

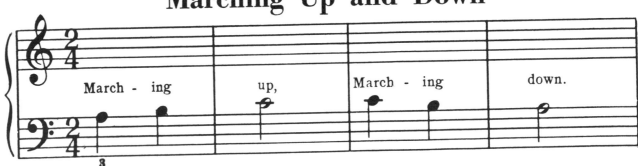

March - ing | up, | March - ing | down.

We have | fun, | 'Round the | town.

Accompaniment

W.M.Co. 7259

Rag-Time Raggles

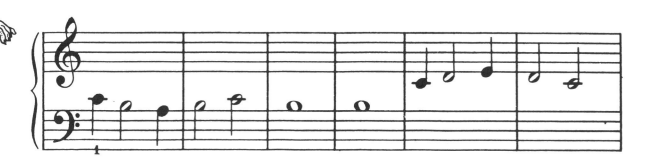

Accompaniment

W.M.Co. 7259

Work Sheet

Read Aloud

The Chimes

Write the new note (G) below.

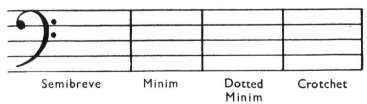

Semibreve	Minim	Dotted Minim	Crotchet

Funny Faces

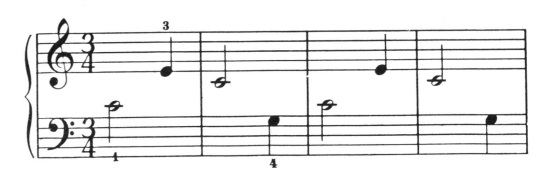

Old MacDonald

Old Mac-Don-ald | had a farm, | Ee-eye, Ee-eye, | oh! And

on this farm he | had some ducks | Ee-eye, Ee-eye, | oh! | Quack, Quack, here | Quack, Quack, there

Ev - 'ry - where a | Quack, Quack, Quack, | Old Mac-Don-ald | had a farm | Ee-eye, Ee-eye, | oh!

W. M. Co. 7259

RESTS

RESTS are signs of silence.　Each kind of Note has a Rest Sign of equal value.

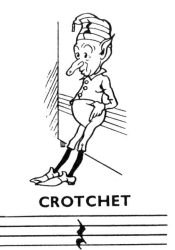

SEMIBREVE

A whole bar's rest

MINIM

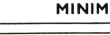

Gets 2 counts

CROTCHET

Gets 1 count

DRAW THE BAR LINES IN THE FOLLOWING EXAMPLE, SO THAT EACH BAR WILL HAVE THE NUMBER OF SILENT COUNTS SHOWN IN THE TIME SIGNATURE

Accompaniment to

"BLOW THE MAN DOWN" (next page)

W. M. Co. 7259

Blow the Man Down

See Accompaniment on opposite page.

W.M.Co. 7259

Read Aloud

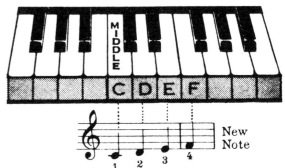

New Note

The Church Organ

Accompaniment

Write the new note (F) below.

Semibreve	Minim	Dotted Minim	Crotchet

W.M.Co. 7259

Read Aloud

Read Aloud

Yankee Doodle

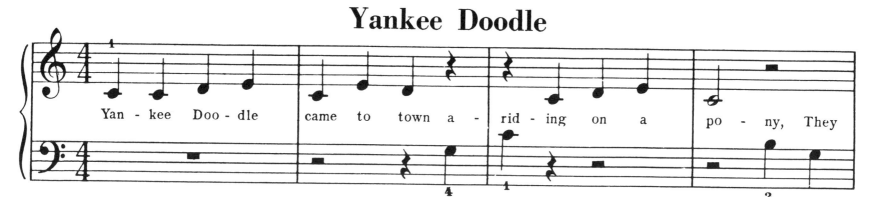

Yan - kee Doo - dle | came to town a - rid - ing on a | po - ny, They

stuck a feath - er | in his hat and | called him Mac - a - ro - ni.

W. M. Co. 7259

Carry Me Back to Old Virginny

James A. Bland

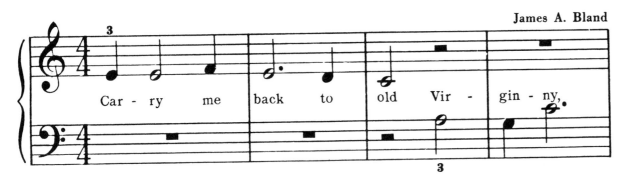

Car - ry me back to old Vir - gin - ny,

There's where the cot - ton and the corn and 'ta - toes grow, There's where the birds war - ble

sweet in the spring-time, There's where the old dar-key's heart am longed to go.

Accompaniment

W.M.Co. 7259

The Old Cotton Picker

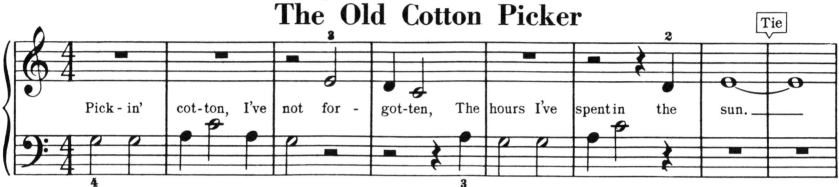

Pick - in' cot-ton, I've not for - got-ten, The hours I've spent in the sun.

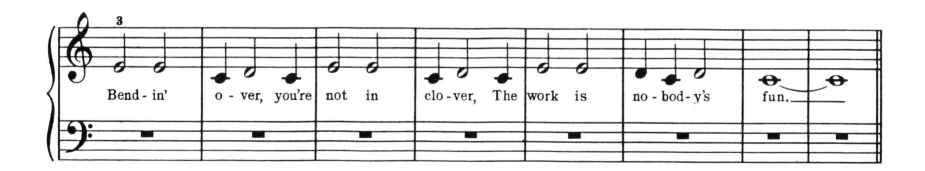

Bend - in' o - ver, you're not in clo - ver, The work is no - bod-y's fun.

Accompaniment

W. M. Co. 7259

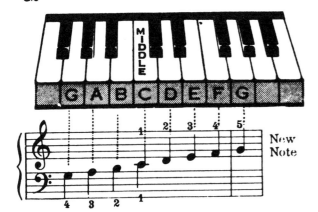

New Note

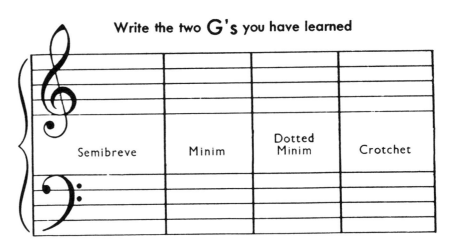

Semibreve	Minim	Dotted Minim	Crotchet

Theme from
"New World" Symphony

Anton Dvořák

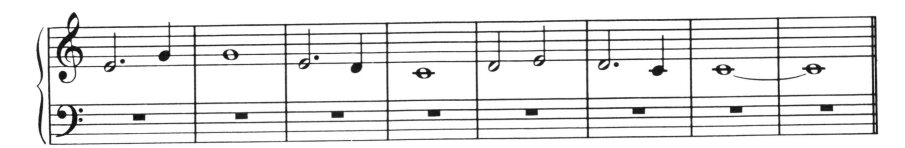

Accompaniment

Bugles!

Row, Row

Row, row, row your boat,

Gen - tly down the stream,

Mer - ri - ly, mer - ri - ly, mer - ri - ly oh! Life is but a dream.

Nobody Knows the Trouble I've Seen

Spiritual

Accompaniment

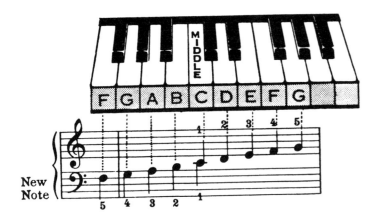

New Note

Write the two F's you have learned

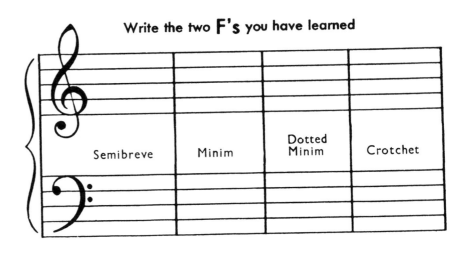

Semibreve	Minim	Dotted Minim	Crotchet

In a Rickshaw

The Banjo Picker

Adapted from
Stephen Foster

Accompaniment

W.M.Co. 7259

Princess Waltz

Accompaniment

WORK SHEET

(Write letter names)

Clap the time (one clap to each count) while reciting the letter-names of the notes.

Afterwards, play the example on your piano, first marking the fingering for each note.

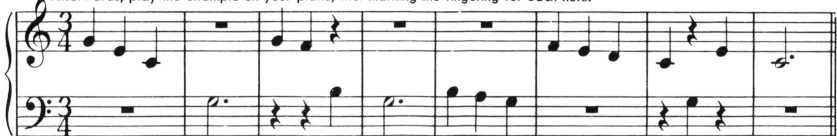

Clap the time and recite the notes as above.

Mark the fingering, then play on the piano.

Printed in Great Britain by Printwise (Haverhill) Limited, Suffolk 11/03 (49327)

Certificate of Merit

This certifies that

....

has successfully completed

PART ONE

OF

John Thompson's
EASIEST PIANO COURSE

and is eligible for promotion to

PART TWO

....

Teacher

Date.............................

W.M.Co. 7259